THE COMPLETE PIANO PLAYER
CHILDREN'S PIECES

Arranged by Kenneth Baker

Marcroft

Wise Publications
London/New York/Sydney

Exclusive distributors:
Music Sales Limited
8/9 Frith Street, London W1V 5TZ, England.
Music Sales Pty Limited
120 Rothschild Street, Rosebery, NSW 2018, Australia.

This book © Copyright 1988 by
Wise Publications
UK ISBN 0.7119.1132.0
Order No. AM65855

Designed by Pearce Marchbank Studio
Compiled by Peter Evans
Arranged by Kenneth Baker

Music Sales complete catalogue lists thousands of titles
and is free from your local music book shop, or direct from
Music Sales Limited. Please send a cheque/postal order
for £1.50 for postage to
Music Sales Limited, 8/9 Frith Street, London W1V 5TZ

Printed and bound in Great Britain by
J.B. Offset Printers (Marks Tey) Limited, Marks Tey.

THE MARVELLOUS TOY

Words & Music by Tom Paxton

Gently ♩ = 84
VERSES

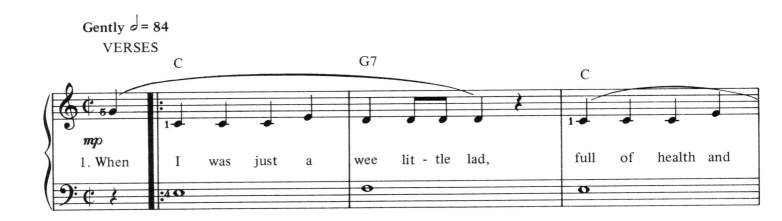

1. When I was just a wee lit-tle lad, full of health and

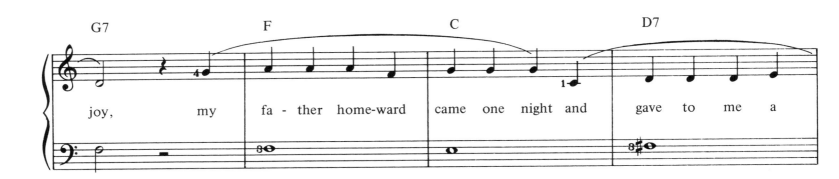

joy, my fa-ther home-ward came one night and gave to me a

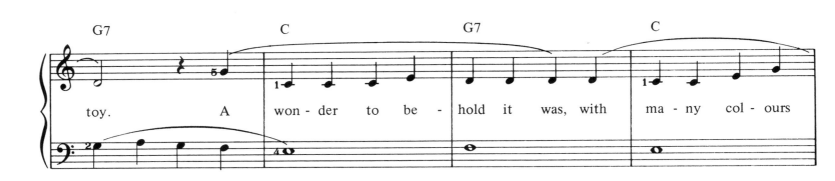

toy. A won-der to be-hold it was, with ma-ny col-ours

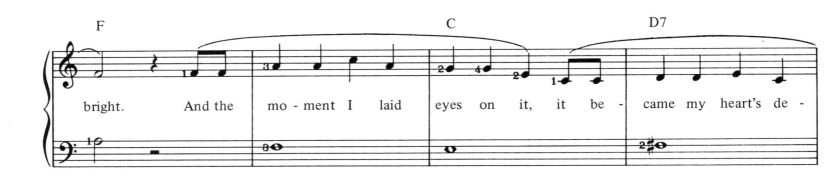

bright. And the mo-ment I laid eyes on it, it be-came my heart's de-

light. It went "zip" when it moved, and "bop" when it stopped, and

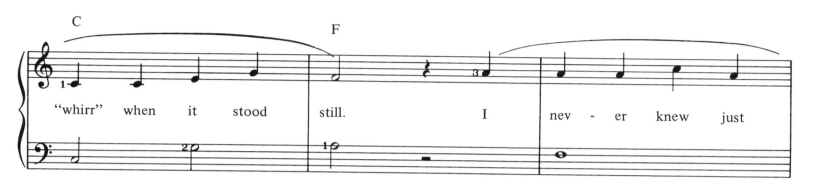

"whirr" when it stood still. I nev - er knew just

what it was, and I guess I nev - er will. The

2. The first time that I picked it up I had a big surprise,
For right on its bottom were two big buttons that looked like big green eyes.
I first pushed one and then the other, and then I twisted its lid,
And when I set it down again, this is what it did. It went
   (To Chorus)

3. It first marched left and then marched right and then marched under a chair,
And when I looked where it had gone, it wasn't even there.
I started to sob and my daddy laughed, for he knew what I would find,
When I turned around, my marvellous toy, chugging from behind. It went
   (To Chorus)

4. Well, the years have gone by too quickly, it seems, and I have my own little boy,
And yesterday I gave to him my marvellous little toy.
His eyes nearly popped right out of his head and he gave a squeal of glee,
Neither one of us knows just what it is, but he loves it just like me.

Last Chorus
   It still goes "zip" when it moves and "bop" when it stops,
   And "whirr" when it stands still,
   I never knew just what it was, and I guess I never will.

THE UNICORN

Words & Music by Shel Silverstein

Calmly ♩ = 63

VERSES

long time a-go when the earth was green, there were more kinds of an-i-mals than

you've ev-er seen. And they'd run a-round free while the world was be-ing born and the

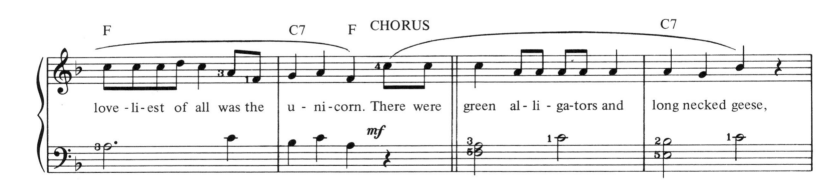

love-li-est of all was the u-ni-corn. There were green al-li-ga-tors and long necked geese,

CHORUS

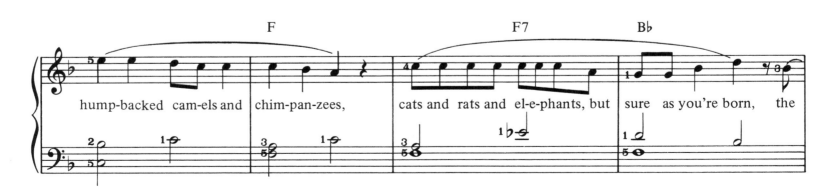

hump-backed cam-els and chim-pan-zees, cats and rats and el-e-phants, but sure as you're born, the

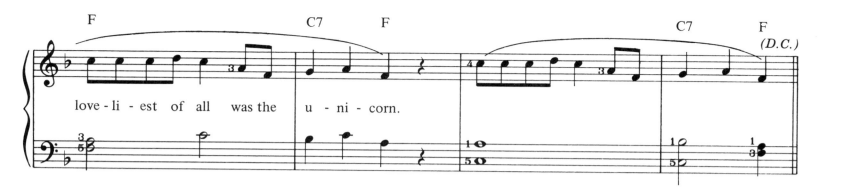

love - li - est of all   was the   u - ni - corn.

2. But the Lord seen some sinnin' and it caused him pain,
   He says, "Stand back, I'm gonna make it rain.
   So hey, Brother Noah, I'll tell you what to do,
   Go and build me a floating zoo."

Chorus:
   "And you take two alligators and a couple of geese,
   Two hump back camels and two chimpanzees,
   Two cats, two rats, two elephants, but sure as you're born,
   Noah, don't you forget my unicorns."

3. Now Noah was there and he answered the callin',
   And he finished up the ark as the rain started fallin',
   Then he marched in the animals two by two,
   And he sung out as they went through:

Chorus:
   "Hey Lord, I got you two alligators and a couple of geese,
   Two hump back camels and two chimpanzees,
   Two cats, two rats, two elephants, but sure as you're born,
   Lord, I just don't see your unicorns."

4. Well, Noah looked out through the drivin' rain,
   But the unicorns was hidin' — playin' silly games,
   They were kickin' and a-splashin' while the rain was pourin',
   Oh them foolish unicorns.

Chorus:
   Repeat 2nd Chorus.

5. Then the ducks started duckin' and the snakes started snakin',
   And the elephants started elephantin' and the boat started shakin',
   The mice started squeakin' and the lions started roarin',
   And everyone's aboard but them unicorns.

Chorus:
   I mean the two alligators and a couple of geese,
   The hump back camels and the chimpanzees,
   Noah cried, "Close the door 'cause the rain is pourin',
   And we just can't wait for them unicorns."

6. And then the ark started movin' and it drifted with the tide,
   And the unicorns looked up from the rock and cried,
   And the water came up and sort of floated them away,
   That's why you've never seen a unicorn to this day.

Chorus:
   You'll see a lot of alligators and a whole mess of geese,
   You'll see hump back camels and chimpanzees,
   You'll see cats and rats and elephants but sure as you're born,
   You're never gonna see no unicorn.

HOW MUCH IS THAT DOGGIE IN THE WINDOW?

Words & Music by Bob Merrill

THE BALLAD OF DAVY CROCKETT

Words by Tom Blackburn
Music by George Bruns

With a swing ♩ = 120

VERSES

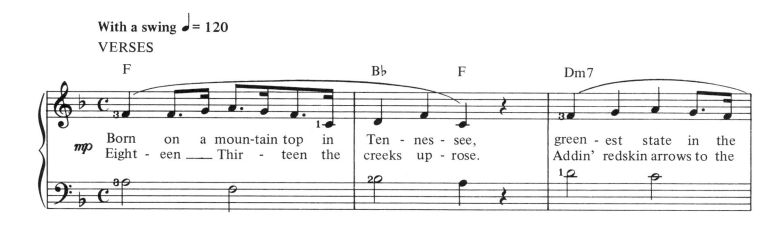

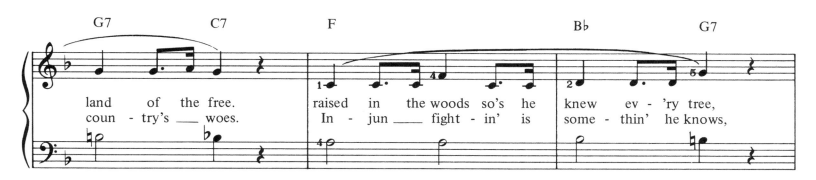

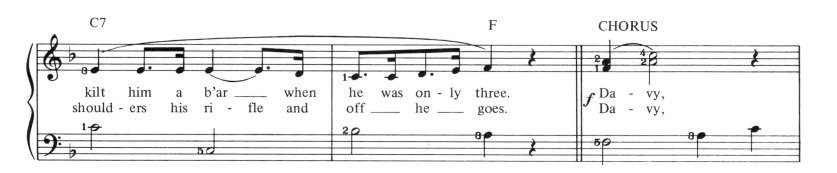

GOING TO THE ZOO

Words & Music by Tom Paxton

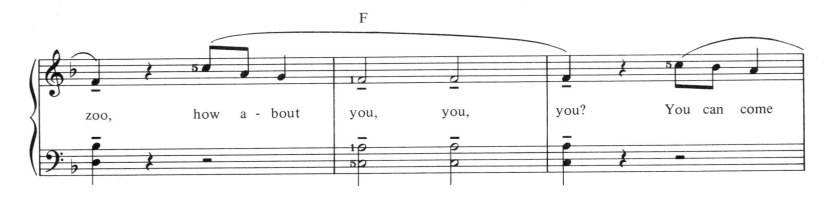

too, too, too, we're go-ing to the zoo, zoo, zoo.

2. See the elephant with the long trunk swingin',
   Great big ears and long trunk swingin'.
   Sniffin' up peanuts with the long trunk swingin',
   We can stay all day.
       We're going to the *(Chorus)*

3. See all the monkeys scritch, scritch, scratchin',
   Jumpin' all around and scritch, scritch, scratchin',
   Hangin' by their long tails scritch, scritch, scratchin',
   We can stay all day.
       We're going to the *(Chorus)*

4. Big black bear all huff, huff, a-puffin',
   Coat's too heavy, he's huff, huff, a-puffin',
   Don't get too near the huff, huff, a-puffin',
   Or you won't stay all day.
       We're going to the *(Chorus)*

5. Seals in the pool all honk, honk, honkin',
   Catchin' fish and honk, honk, honkin',
   Little seals honk, honk, honkin', *(high pitched voice)*
   We can stay all day.
       We're going to the *(Chorus)*

6. *(Slower tempo)*
   We stayed all day and I'm gettin' sleepy,
   Sittin' in the car gettin' sleep, sleep, sleepy,
   Home already and I'm sleep, sleep, sleepy,
   We have stayed all day.
       We're going to the *(Chorus)*

7. Mamma's taking us to the zoo tomorrow, zoo tomorrow, zoo tomorrow,
   Mamma's taking us to the zoo tomorrow,
   We can stay all day.
       We've been to the zoo, zoo, zoo,
       So have you, you, you,
       You came too, too, too,
       We've been to the zoo, zoo, zoo.

GRANDMA'S FEATHER BED

Words & Music by Jim Connor

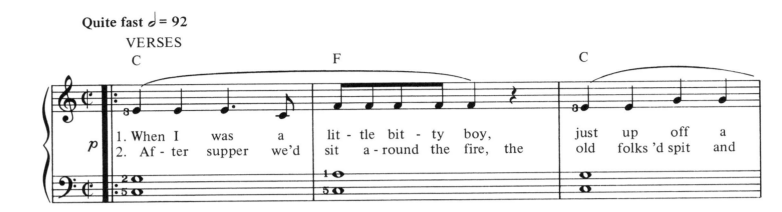

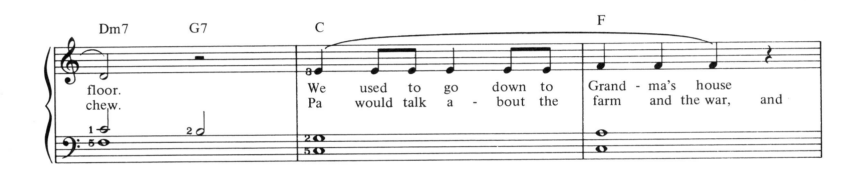

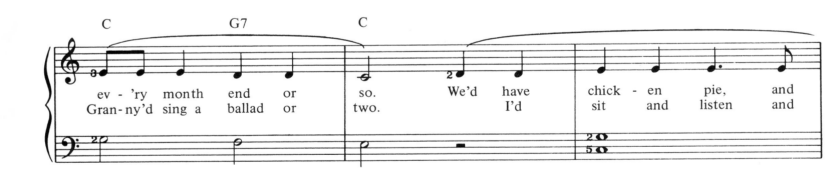

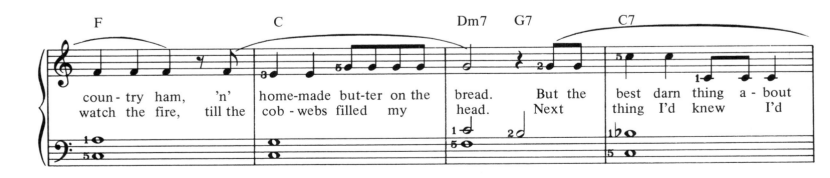

13

THREE LITTLE FISHES (ITTY BITTY POO)

Words & Music by Saxie Dowell

With gusto ♩ = 126

VERSES

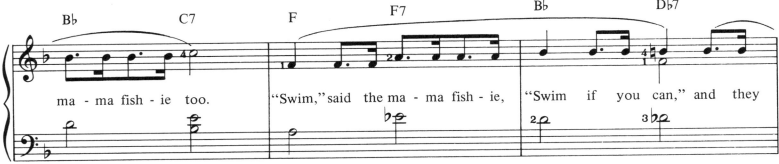

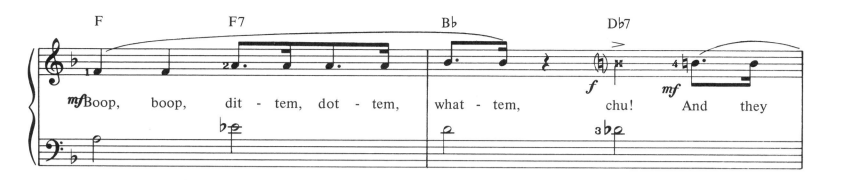

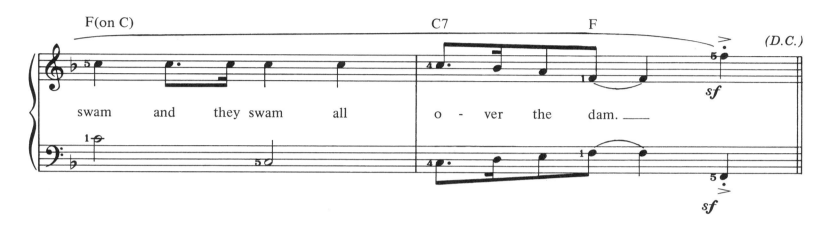

2. "Stop," said the mama fishie, "or you will get lost,"
But the three little fishies didn't want to be bossed.
So the three little fishies went off on a spree,
And they swam and they swam right out to the sea.
    Boop, boop, dittem, dottem whattem, chu!
    Boop, boop, dittem, dottem whattem, chu!
    Boop, boop, dittem, dottem whattem, chu!
And they swam and they swam right out to the sea.

3. "Whee!" Yelled the little fishies "here's a lot of fun,
We'll swim in the sea till the day is done."
So they swam and they swam and it was a lark,
Till all of a sudden they met a SHARK.
    Boop, boop, dittem, dottem whattem, chu!
    Boop, boop, dittem, dottem whattem, chu!
    Boop, boop, dittem, dottem whattem, chu!
Till all of a sudden they met a SHARK.

4. "Help!" Cried the little fishies, "look at the whales."
And quick as they could they turned on their tails.
And back to the pool in the meadow they swam,
And they swam and they swam back over the dam,
    Boop, boop, dittem, dottem whattem, chu!
    Boop, boop, dittem, dottem whattem, chu!
    Boop, boop, dittem, dottem whattem, chu!
And they swam and they swam back over the dam.

15

NURSERY RHYME MEDLEY

(COMPRISING BAA BAA BLACK SHEEP, POLLY PUT THE KETTLE ON, GOOSEY GOOSEY GANDER, TOM TOM THE PIPER'S SON, SING A SONG OF SIXPENCE, BOBBY SHAFTOE).

Polly, put the kettle on

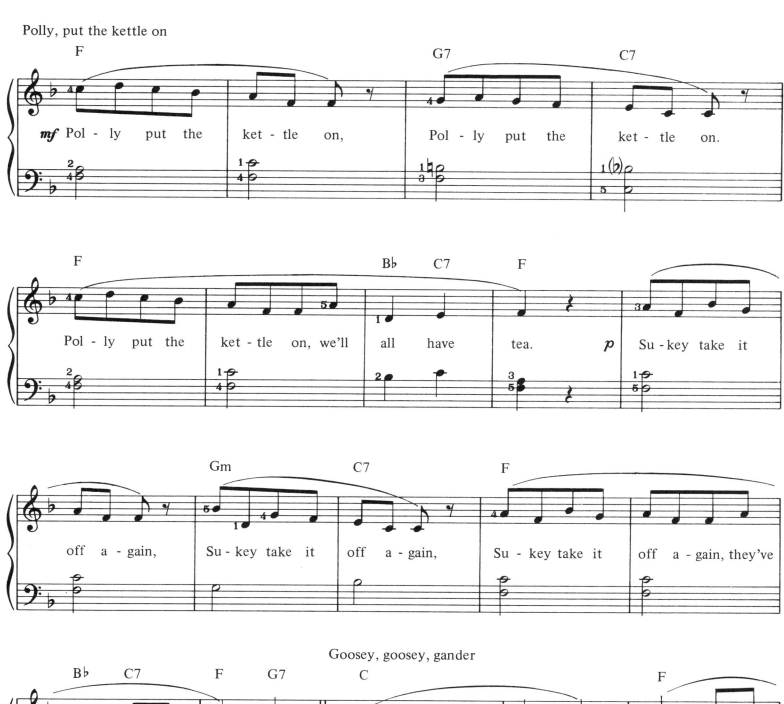

Pol - ly put the ket - tle on, Pol - ly put the ket - tle on.

Pol - ly put the ket - tle on, we'll all have tea. Su - key take it

off a - gain, Su - key take it off a - gain, Su - key take it off a - gain, they've

Goosey, goosey, gander

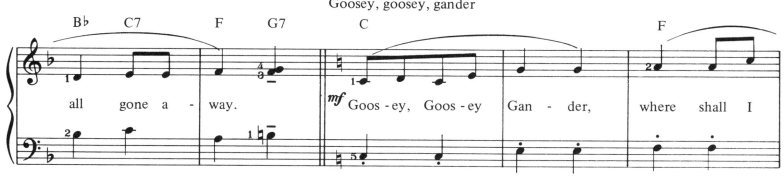

all gone a - way. Goos - ey, Goos - ey Gan - der, where shall I

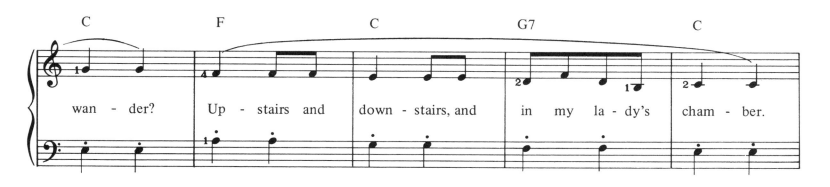

wan - der? Up - stairs and down - stairs, and in my la - dy's cham - ber.

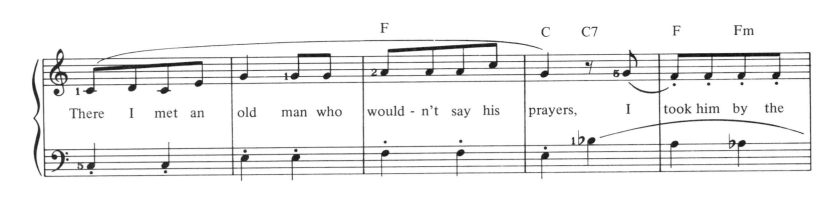

There I met an old man who would-n't say his prayers, I took him by the

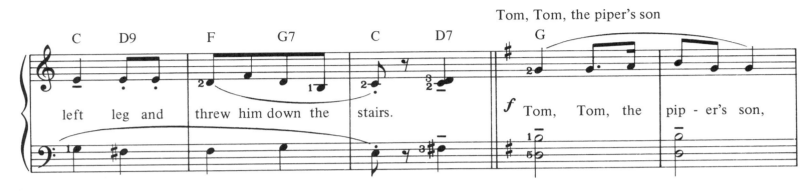

left leg and threw him down the stairs.

Tom, Tom, the piper's son

Tom, Tom, the pip-er's son,

stole a pig and a - way he run. The pig was eat, and Tom was beat, and Tom went howl-ing

Sing a song of sixpence

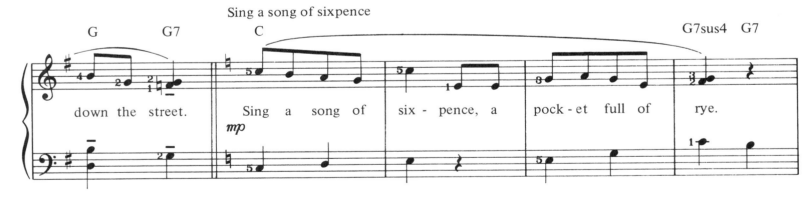

down the street. Sing a song of six - pence, a pock - et full of rye.

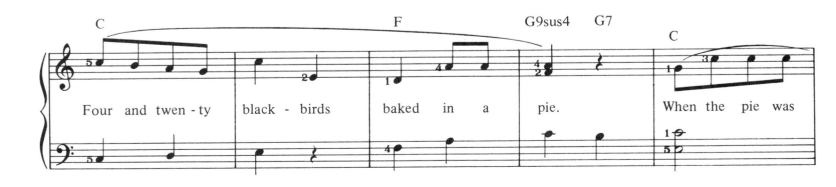

Four and twen - ty black - birds baked in a pie. When the pie was

LITTLE WHITE DUCK

Words by Walt Barrows
Music by Bernard Zaritzky

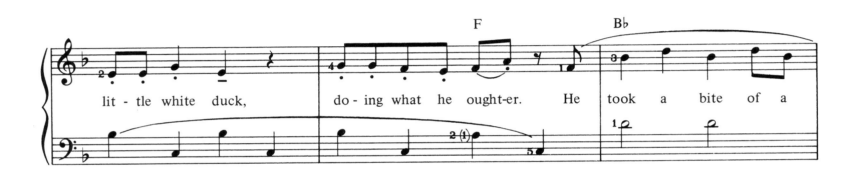

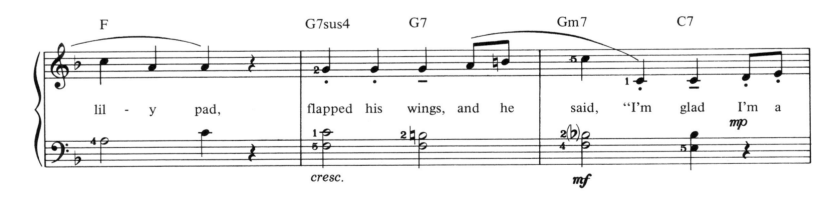

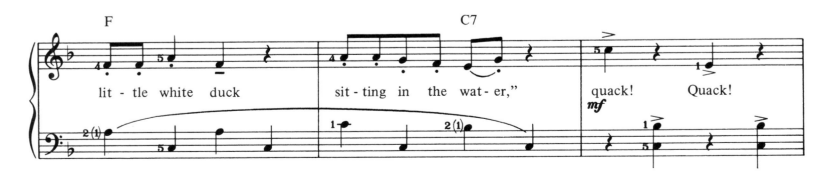

2. (There's a) little green frog swimming in the water,
   A little green frog doing what he oughter,
   He jumped right off of the lily pad,
   That the little duck bit, and he said:
   "I'm glad I'm a little green frog swimming in the water."
   Glumph! Glumph! Glumph!

3. (There's a) little black bug floating in the water,
   A little black bug doing what he oughter,
   He tickled the frog on the lily pad,
   That the little duck bit, and he said:
   "I'm glad I'm a little black bug floating on the water,"
   Chirp! Chirp! Chirp!

4. (There's a) little red snake lying in the water,
   Little red snake doing what he oughter,
   He frightened the duck and the frog so bad,
   Hit the little bug, and he said:
   "I'm glad I'm a little red snake lying in the water,"
   Sss! Sss! Sss!

5. (Now there's) nobody left sitting in the water,
   Nobody left doing what he oughter,
   There's nothing left but the lily pad,
   The duck and the frog ran away, it's sad
   That there's nobody left sitting in the water,
   Boo! Hoo! Hoo!

FOOD GLORIOUS FOOD

Words & Music by Lionel Bart

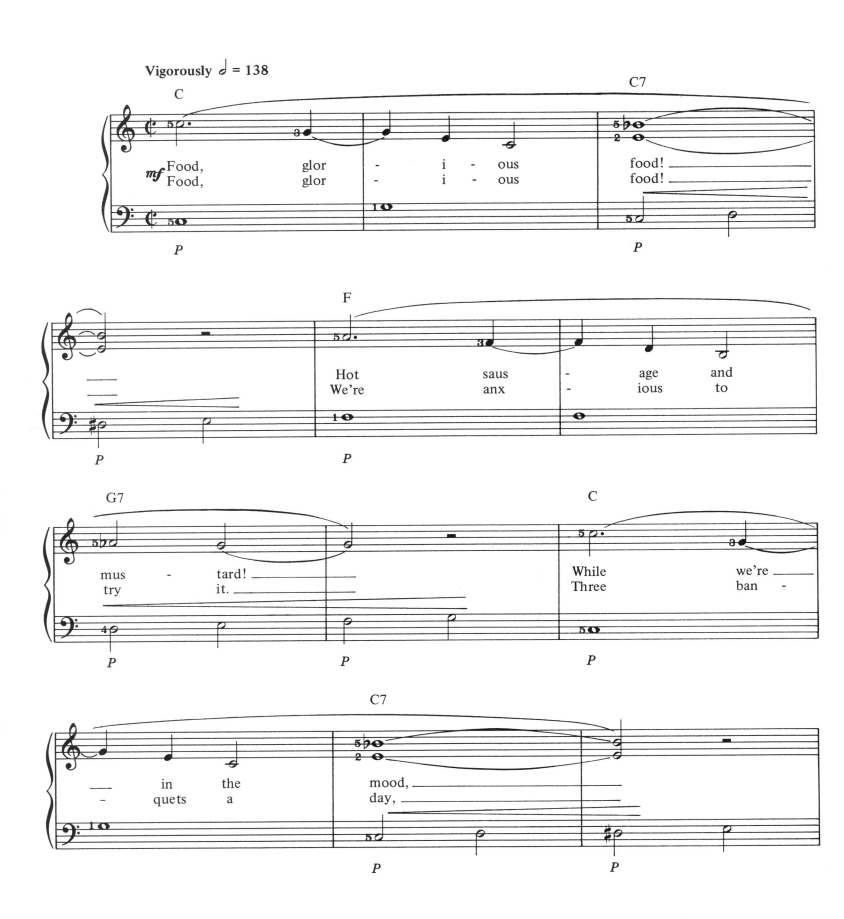

THE LONELY BULL (EL SOLO TORO)

By Sol Lake

DADDY WOULDN'T BUY ME A BOW WOW

Words & Music by Joseph Tabrar

CHICK CHICK CHICKEN

Words & Music by Fred Holt, Thos McGhee & Irving King

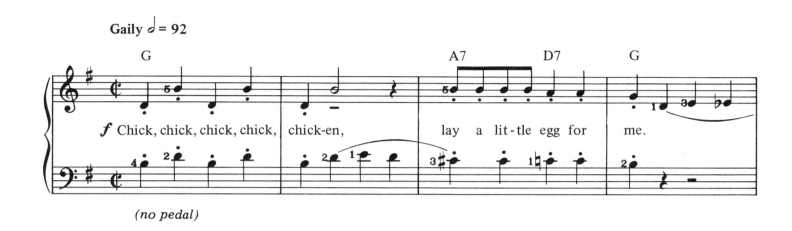

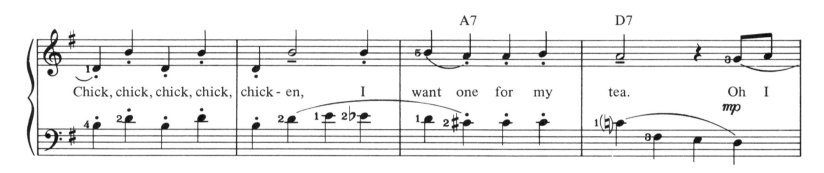

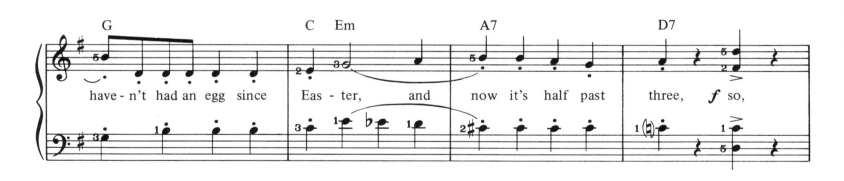

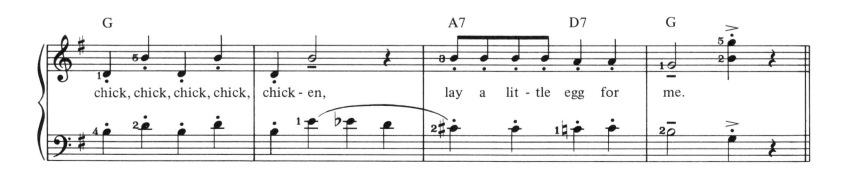

EVERYTHING IS BEAUTIFUL

Words & Music by Ray Stevens

in its own way. _____ Like a star-ry
sum - mer night, or a snow cov-ered win - ter's ___ day. _____
___ Ev - 'ry - bo - dy's beau - ti - ful _____ in their own
way. _____ Un - der God's __ hea - ven the
world's gon - na find _____ a - way. _____

29

ALLEY CAT
Words & Music by Frank Bjorn

THE CANDY MAN

Words & Music by Leslie Bricusse & Anthony Newley

D.C. al Coda

⊕ **CODA**

slowly (ad lib.)

(a tempo)

world taste good. ___ The can-dy man makes ev-'ry-thing he bakes sat-is-fy-ing and de-li-cious. Talk a-bout your child-hood wish-es, you can e-ven eat the dish-es.

world ___ taste good. ___ And the world tastes good 'cause the can-dy man thinks ___ it should. ___

HE'S A TRAMP

Words & Music by Peggy Lee & Sonny Burke

A SPOONFUL OF SUGAR

Words & Music by Richard M. Sherman & Robert B. Sherman

37

THE UGLY BUG BALL

Words & Music by Richard M. Sherman & Robert B. Sherman

CONSIDER YOURSELF

Words & Music by Lionel Bart

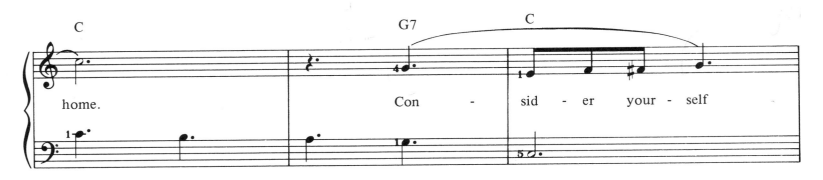

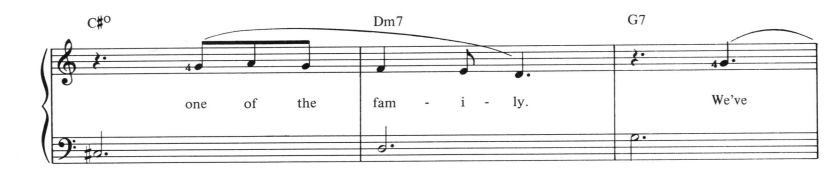

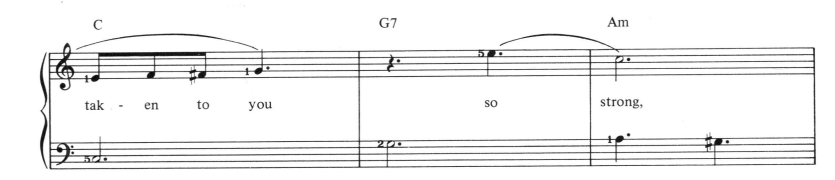

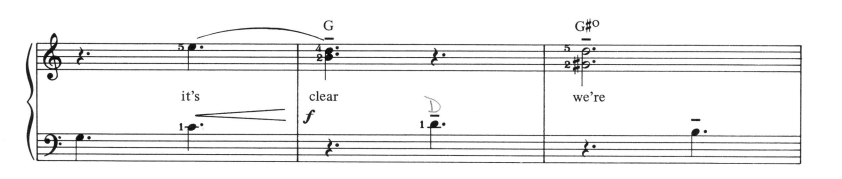

it's clear we're

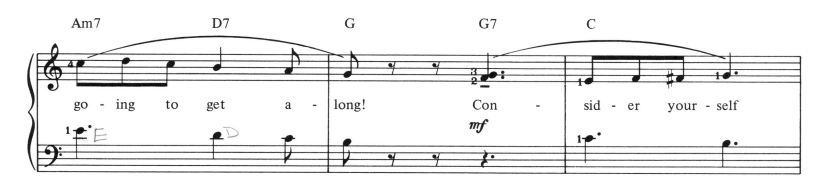

go - ing to get a - long! Con - sid - er your - self

well in. Con -

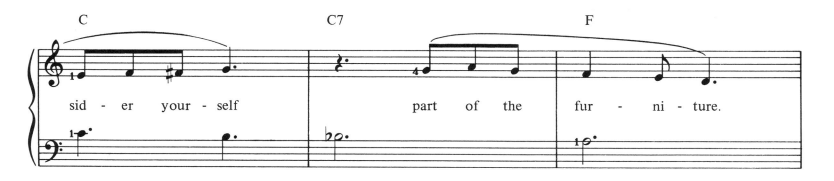

sid - er your - self part of the fur - ni - ture.

There is - n't a lot to

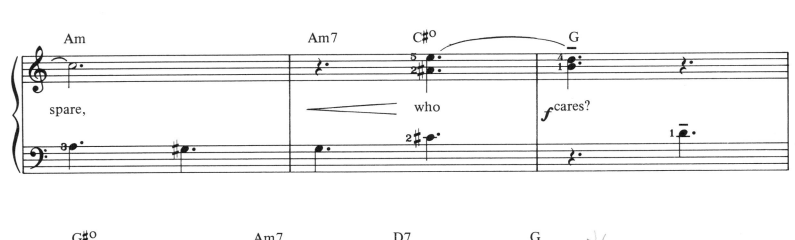

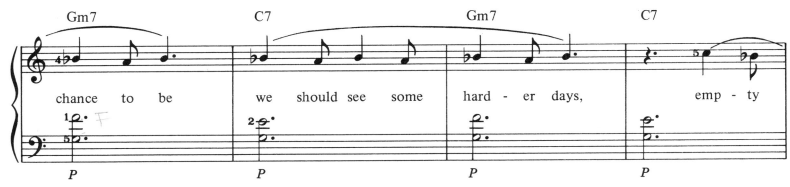

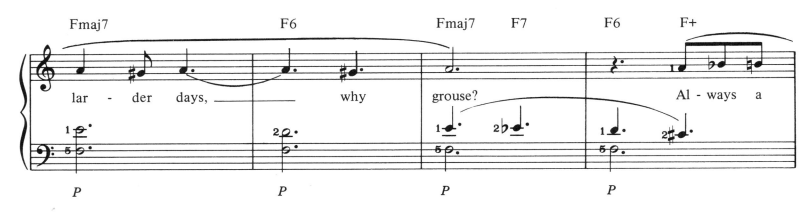

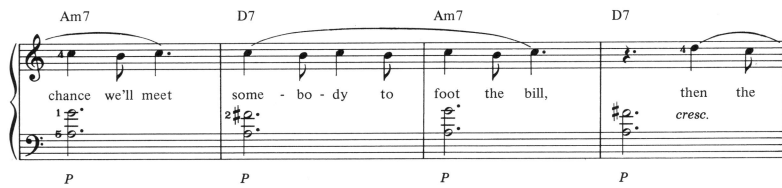

PARADE OF THE TIN SOLDIERS

By Leon Jessel

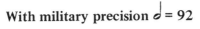

With military precision ♩ = 92

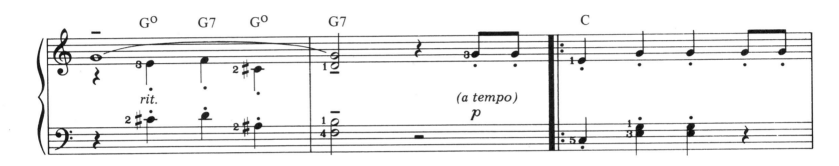

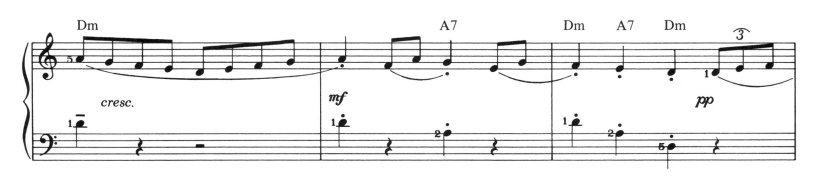

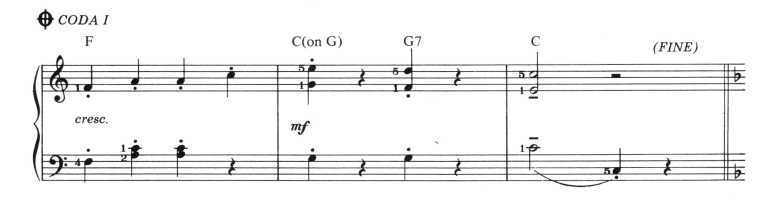

47